This book belongs to:

____

The Furry Arms Hotel

Written by Susan Hood
Illustrated by Tom Brannon

Printed in China
ISBN: 1-40379-200-3

CE11822/0709/SEP

One day a cute, furry black puppy bounded into the lobby of the Furry Arms hotel. The puppy was running so fast that he slid—*whoosh!*—across the lobby floor.

A bell-dinger rushed up to greet the new guest.

"Hello, sir," said the dinger. "Would you like a room? Right this way, please."

As the dinger led the way to the front desk, the puppy stopped. He spotted a cute furry red monster playing with baby Natasha. He was the little monster who liked to play hide-and-seek all around the neighborhood.

The little puppy hid fast. He liked to play, too!

The dinger dinged his dinger at the front desk.

"What's all that racket about?" demanded Sherry Netherland, the owner of the hotel.

"This cute little black puppy would like a room," said the dinger.

"I don't see any cute little black puppy," said Sherry.

Then Elmo ran up to the desk.

"Did Miss Netherland say a cute little black *puppy*?"

Elmo looked everywhere for the puppy—even behind the desk and in the mail slots.

"May Elmo look upstairs?" he asked.

"Oh, all right," said Sherry. "But take Benny the Bellhop with you."

“Is there a puppy in here?” asked Benny the Bellhop, opening a hotel room door.

“No,” said Elmo, shaking his head. “Puppies do not live in the desert.”

"What about here?" asked Benny as he opened the door to a very fishy room.

"No," replied Elmo. "Puppies do not live in the ocean."

"How about here?" asked Benny.

"No," said Elmo. "Puppies do not live in a rainforest, either. But what is in that last room down the hall?"

Puppies! There were big puppies, small puppies, fat puppies, and skinny puppies. Brown puppies, white puppies, yellow puppies, and spotted puppies.

But Elmo did not see the little black puppy.

“Oh, well,” Elmo sighed. “Elmo guesses the little lost puppy did not check in to the Furry Arms hotel. Now it’s time for Elmo to go home. Bye-bye, Baby Natasha.”

“Bah-bah!” Baby Natasha waved.

As he stepped into the elevator, Elmo murmured, “Where could that puppy be . . . ?”

1 2 3 4

"Puppy!" giggled Baby Natasha.

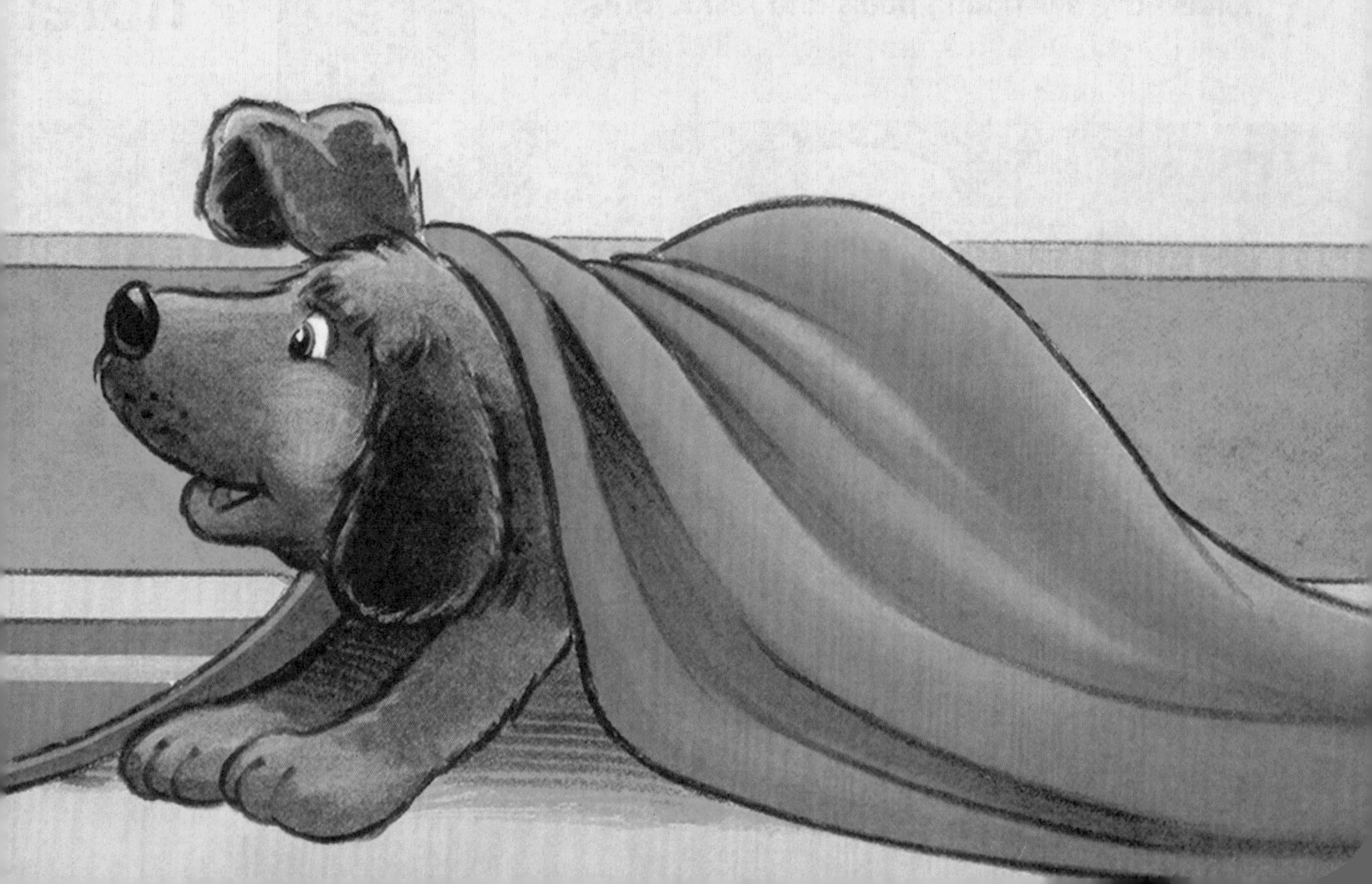

Elmo's Everyday Words

lobby

The room you walk into when you enter the front door of a building.
What kinds of things would you find in a lobby?

hotel

A building where you can get a room to sleep in when you are traveling or on vacation. Some hotels have swimming pools and restaurants.
How do you think a hotel room is different from your bedroom?

greet

To welcome someone or say hello in a friendly way.
You can greet with a handshake, a hug, or just a hello. How do you greet a friend?

front desk

The place in the lobby of a hotel where guests check in, ask questions, get messages, and check out.
Name some things that you think you might find at a front desk.

hide-and-seek

A game where one person finds a place to hide and another person tries to find him or her.
What games do you like to play?

A place you can put letters, cards, and notes.
Make a card for someone special and mail it.

mail slot

bellhop

Someone who works in a hotel whose job is to help the guests, carrying luggage or showing guests to their room.
Pretend to be a bellhop. What would you do?

A place that is hot and dry with very little rain.
What would you wear if you visited the desert?

desert

ocean

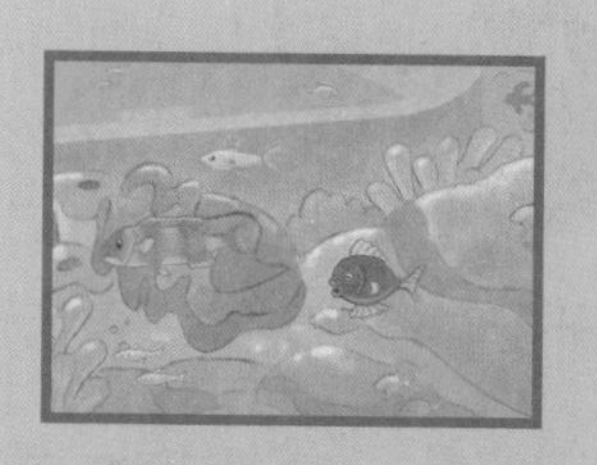

A big body of saltwater.
What types of animals live in the ocean?

A forest that is in a rainy place (often tropical and warm).
Many lizards and birds live in the rainforest. What other animals might live there?

rainforest

elevator

A moving room that carries people up and down to different floors in a building.
Pretend you are in an elevator.
What floor are you going to?

Big Bird's BIG Ideas

whoosh

A noise that is made by moving air, like the wind or something moving very fast.
Make a "whoosh" sound!

owner

A person who has something that belongs to him or her.
Are you a pet owner?

spotted

To have lots of spots, like a Dalmatian dog or a leopard.
Draw a picture of an animal that has lots of spots!

neighborhood

The people and places that are near your home.
Many neighborhoods have a hotel nearby where people can stay when they are visiting.
Have you stayed at a hotel? What did you do while you were there?

Do You See What I See?

What words would YOU use to talk about these things that you might see in a hotel? Think of as many different words as you can. Share your words with a friend!